MW00647069

ANATOMY & PHYSIOLOGY

The Best and Most Effective Way to Learn the Anatomy and Physiology of the Human Body

Workbook

M. Mastenbjörk M.D.
S. Meloni M.D.

Medical Creations

© **Copyright 2024 by Medical Creations® - All rights reserved.**

This document is geared towards providing exact and reliable information in regards to the topic and issue covered. The publication is sold with the idea that the publisher is not required to render accounting, officially permitted, or otherwise, qualified services. If advice is necessary, legal or professional, a practiced individual in the profession should be ordered.

- From a Declaration of Principles which was accepted and approved equally by a Committee of the American Bar Association and a Committee of Publishers and Associations.

In no way is it legal to reproduce, duplicate, or transmit any part of this document in either electronic means or in printed format. Recording of this publication is strictly prohibited and any storage of this document is not allowed unless with written permission from the publisher. All rights reserved.

The information provided herein is stated to be truthful and consistent, in that any liability, in terms of inattention or otherwise, by any usage or abuse of any policies, processes, or directions contained within is the solitary and utter responsibility of the recipient reader. Under no circumstances will any legal responsibility or blame be held against the publisher for any reparation, damages, or monetary loss due to the information herein, either directly or indirectly.

Respective authors own all copyrights not held by the publisher.

The information herein is offered for informational purposes solely, and is universal as so. The presentation of the information is without contract or any type of guarantee assurance.

The trademarks that are used are without any consent, and the publication of the trademark is without permission or backing by the trademark owner. All trademarks and brands within this book are for clarifying purposes only and are the owned by the owners themselves, not affiliated with this document.

YOU MIGHT ALSO NEED

Medical Terminology:
The Best and Most Effective Way
to Memorize, Pronounce and
Understand Medical Terms
(2nd Edition)

Medical Terminology:
The Best and Most Effective
Way to Memorize, Pronounce
and Understand Medical Terms:
Workbook

Scan the QR Code

JOIN OUR 7-DAY
MEDICAL TERMINOLOGY COURSE

If you prefer to learn by watching videos
this course is for you!

Use code "**medtermbook**" for a discount

FREE GIFT

GET ONE OF THESE EBOOKS FOR FREE:

Anatomy & Physiology Rationales
Medical Reference Pamphlet
ACLS ebook
Medical Terminology Digital Pamphlet
Neurology ebook
Mini Medical Dictionary
ECG - Digital Reference Pamphlet
Pulmonology ebook

Scan the following QR Code:

You will be redirected to our website.
Follow the instructions to claim your free gift.

Contents

INTRODUCTION

The fundamental blocks for any clinical career are rooted in the understanding of anatomy and physiology. Only when we have a good understanding of the normal structure and function of the human body can we identify any anomalies and pathology.

Besides, learning anatomy and physiology is a great way of getting introduced to many medical terms. However, if your primary goal is to improve your medical terminology skills, our popular handbooks on medical terminology can help you. These handbooks also provide a great introduction to general topics such as anatomical planes and body systems, which can assist you when studying anatomy and physiology.

If you believe you've got your anatomy and physiology mastered, then dive into this workbook and test your knowledge with the given exercises.

We wish you good luck in your endeavor!

Cell, Cell Membrane and Nucleic Acids

EXERCISE 1 - LABEL THE PICTURE

The following is a schematic illustration of a liver cell (hepatocyte). Can you name its different components?

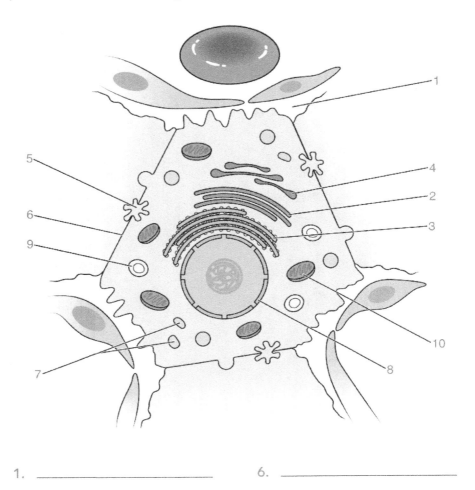

1. _____   6. _____

2. _____   7. _____

3. _____   8. _____

4. _____   9. _____

5. _____   10. _____

EXERCISE 2 - MATCH THE COLUMNS

Pick up options from the last column. Place them in the 'Correct match' column in an order that matches them up with the terms in the first column.

	Cell component	Correct match	Function
11.	Cell membrane		Detoxification
12.	Mitochondria		Lipid synthesis
13.	Ribosomes		Ribosomal assembly
14.	Golgi complex		Barrier and transport
15.	Nucleus		Protein synthesis
16.	Lysosomes		Regulation and cell division
17.	Cytoskeleton		Transport and packaging
18.	Microbodies		Energy synthesis
19.	Nucleolus		Digestion
20.	Smooth endoplasmic reticulum		Shape and movement

EXERCISE 3 – TRUE OR FALSE

The following statements describe the structure and function of the cell membrane, but not all of them are accurate. Mark them as true (T) or false (F) accordingly.

21. The cell membrane is also called the cell wall.

22. The cell membrane consists of a phospholipid bilayer.

23. It is impermeable to lipid-soluble substances.

24. Ion channels are made from integral proteins in the cell membrane.

25. It can engulf extracellular material through a process called endocytosis.

26. Cholesterol is dispersed throughout the cell membrane.

27. Cholesterol influences the fluidity of the cell membrane.

28. The cell membrane of nerve cells is called sarcolemma.

29. Oxygen needs a transport protein to move across the cell membrane.

30. Carbon dioxide moves across the cell membrane by passive diffusion.

EXERCISE 4 - FILL IN THE BLANKS

31. Genetic material is essentially _____ acids.

32. Nucleic acids are made up of nucleotides. Each nucleotide is made of three components: a 5-carbon sugar, a _____ group and a nitrogenous base.

33. In DNA, the sugar is _____.

34. The five primary nucleobases are: adenine, _____ , guanine, thymine and uracil.

35. Of the nucleobases, thymine occurs only in DNA and _____ occurs only in RNA.

36. They are named nucleic acids because they were initially discovered inside the _____.

37. All life forms possess nucleic acids, including _____ which some experts consider to be non-living.

38. DNA molecules are _____-stranded.

39. _____ refers to the creation of messenger RNA (mRNA) from a section of DNA.

40. Amino acids to be used in protein synthesis are carried by _____.

EXERCISE 5 - MCQs

41. Which one of the following terms denotes chemical reactions in cells that breakdown large molecules into smaller ones and release energy?

    a. Metabolism
    b. Autophagy
    c. Anabolism
    d. Catabolism

42. Which one of the following cellular organelles is responsible for "cellular respiration"?

    a. Ribosome
    b. Smooth endoplasmic reticulum
    c. Mitochondrion
    d. Lysosome

43. Where in the cell does glycolysis take place?

    a. Nucleus
    b. Cytoplasm
    c. Cell membrane
    d. Mitochondria

44. Which one of the following molecules represents the entry point of the Kreb's cycle?

    a. Pyruvate
    b. Citric acid
    c. Succinyl CoA
    d. Malate

45. Anaerobic respiration leads to the buildup of which one of the following?

    a. Citric acid
    b. Glucose
    c. Lactic acid
    d. ATP

46. Cells from which layer of the embryo develop into muscles and bone?

    a.   Endoderm
    b.   Mesoderm
    c.   Ectoderm
    d.   Placental cells

47. The outer surfaces of the phospholipid bilayer of the cell membrane are:

    a.   Fatty acid chains
    b.   Nonpolar
    c.   Hydrophilic
    d.   Hydrophobic

48. Water osmosis across the cell membrane is dependent on small proteins called:

    a.   Proton pumps
    b.   G proteins
    c.   Aquaporins
    d.   Glycocalyx

49. A cell placed in a solution was observed to swell up and burst. The solution must be:

    a.   Hypotonic
    b.   Isotonic
    c.   Hypertonic
    d.   Normal saline

50. Which one of the following terms describes the process of "cellular drinking"?

    a.   Exocytosis
    b.   Endocytosis
    c.   Phagocytosis
    d.   Pinocytosis

51. During cell division, which one of the following materials condenses and forms chromosomes?

    a. Protoplasm
    b. Chromatin
    c. Nucleolus
    d. Nucleoplasm

52. Which fibrous proteins build the cytoskeleton of the cell?

    a. Microfilaments
    b. Intermediate filaments
    c. Microtubules
    d. All of the above

53. The inner membrane of the mitochondrion has inward folds. These are called:

    a. Microvilli
    b. Brush border
    c. Cristae
    d. Plasmalemma

54. The part of the cell cycle during which cells aren't dividing is called:

    a. Apoptosis
    b. Prophase
    c. Interphase
    d. Metaphase

55. The part of the cell cycle during which chromosomes line up in the middle of the cell is called:

    a. Apoptosis
    b. Prophase
    c. Interphase
    d. Metaphase

Skin and Musculoskeletal System

EXERCISE 1 - LABEL THE PICTURE

The following is a diagrammatic representation of the pelvic (hip) girdle.
Can you name its different parts?

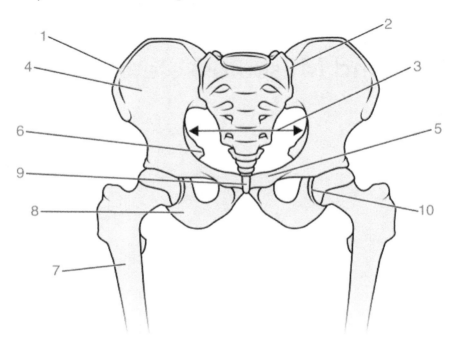

1. _____   6. _____

2. _____   7. _____

3. _____   8. _____

4. _____   9. _____

5. _____   10. _____

EXERCISE 2 – MATCH THE COLUMNS

Do you know the nerve supply of the muscles of the upper limb? Choose the right option from the last column and place it adjacent to the appropriate muscle in the "Correct match" column.

	Muscle	Correct match	Nerve
11.	Biceps brachii		Long thoracic
12.	Deltoid		Accessory
13.	Latissimus dorsi		Radial
14.	Serratus anterior		Radial, deep branch
15.	Trapezius		Ulnar
16.	Triceps		Musculocutaneous
17.	Pronator teres		Ulnar, deep branch
18.	Extensor digitorum		Thoracodorsal
19.	Flexor carpi ulnaris		Axillary
20.	The interossei		Median

EXERCISE 3 - TRUE OR FALSE

The following are some statements about our integumentary system. But not all of them are correct. Mark them with T (for true) or F (for false) accordingly.

21. The skin is considered to be the largest organ of the human body.

22. It is made up of two layers: epidermis and hypodermis.

23. Pacinian corpuscles in the skin respond to changes in temperature.

24. The epidermis does not contain any blood vessels.

25. Stratum lucidum is thick and opaque because it contains keratin.

26. Skin color depends on a pigment called melanin.

27. Sebaceous glands of the skin have an oily secretion.

28. Nociception is another term for sensing pressure.

29. Eccrine sweat glands are found primarily in the armpits.

30. Nails are hard because they contain carotene.

EXERCISE 4 - FILL IN THE BLANKS

Joints are a common and essential feature of the musculoskeletal system. They make movement possible. Test your knowledge about joints with the following questions.

31. The study of joints is called _____.

32. Some joints are immovable, they are known as _____.

33. A ball and socket type joint, such as the hip joint, allows movement in _____ planes.

34. Movement at a joint that is away from the midline of the body is termed as _____.

35. The anterior and posterior cruciate ligaments help to stabilize the _____ joint.

36. A gomphosis is a fibrous joint that binds the _____ to their bony sockets.

37. Articular cartilage, which is basically _____ cartilage, lines the bones in a synovial joint.

38. The _____ muscle is the strongest flexor of the elbow joint.

39. The knee joint is formed between the femur, _____ and patella.

40. The elbow joint is a _____ joint and therefore uniaxial.

15

EXERCISE 5 - MCQs

41. The red bone marrow inside some bones is the site of production of blood cells through a process called:

    a. Homeostasis
    b. Erythropoiesis
    c. Hematopoiesis
    d. Hemostasis

42. What type of a bone is the scapula categorized as?

    a. Long
    b. Short
    c. Flat
    d. Irregular

43. The connective tissue covering of bones is called:

    a. Sharpey's fibers
    b. Compact bone
    c. Periosteum
    d. Perichondrium

44. The shaft of a long bone is called:

    a. Medullary cavity
    b. Epiphysis
    c. Haversian canal
    d. Diaphysis

45. Which one of the following type of bone cells is responsible for bone resorption?

    a. Osteocytes
    b. Osteoblasts
    c. Osteoclasts
    d. Fibroblasts

46. In endochondral ossification, bones develop through the calcification of:

   a. Fibrous membranes
   b. Muscle sheets
   c. Hyaline cartilage
   d. Collagen

47. Which one of the following skull bones makes up the forehead?

   a. Nasal bone
   b. Zygomatic process
   c. Occipital bone
   d. Frontal bone

48. All of the following are small bones (ossicles) found inside the ear EXCEPT:

   a. Malleus
   b. Concha
   c. Incus
   d. Stapes

49. Which one of the following is a function of skeletal muscles?

   a. Posture
   b. Locomotion
   c. Heat production
   d. All of the above

50. The more movable attachment of a muscle is called its:

   a. Insertion
   b. Origin
   c. Tendon
   d. Joint

51. The cytoplasm of muscle fibers is called:

   a.   Protoplasm
   b.   Nucleoplasm
   c.   Sarcolemma
   d.   Sarcoplasm

52. Which one of the following types of muscle tissues is striated?

   a.   Skeletal muscle
   b.   Cardiac muscle
   c.   Smooth muscle
   d.   Both a and b

53. Which one of the following types of muscle tissues is responsible for peristalsis?

   a.   Skeletal muscle
   b.   Cardiac muscle
   c.   Smooth muscle
   d.   Both a and b

54. In a sarcomere, what lies in the middle of the I band?

   a.   M line
   b.   Z line
   c.   H zone
   d.   A band

55. The neurotransmitter typically released at the motor end plate in skeletal muscles is:

   a.   Adrenaline
   b.   Acetylcholine
   c.   Serotonin
   d.   GABA

Cardiovascular System

EXERCISE 1 - LABEL THE PICTURE

Label the different structures of the heart in the diagrammatic illustration below.

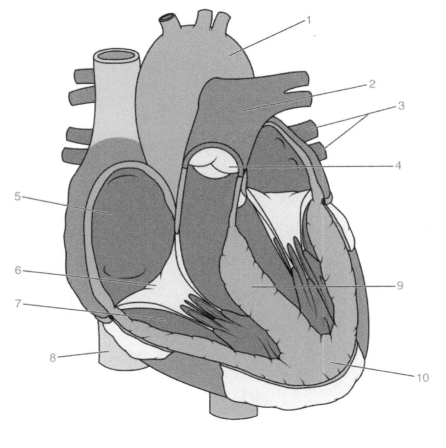

1. _____   6. _____

2. _____   7. _____

3. _____   8. _____

4. _____   9. _____

5. _____   10. _____

EXERCISE 2 – MATCH THE COLUMNS

This exercise requires you to match an artery with its corresponding branch. For instance, if the given artery is the arch of aorta and the left subclavian artery is listed in the right column, you would match it with the arch of aorta as we know that it is its branch.

	Artery	Correct match	Branch
11.	Popliteal artery		Vertebral artery
12.	External carotid artery		Right coronary artery
13.	Internal carotid artery		Lateral thoracic artery
14.	Abdominal aorta		Superior gluteal artery
15.	Axillary artery		Anterior tibial artery
16.	Arch of aorta		Radial artery
17.	Internal iliac artery		Maxillary artery
18.	Subclavian artery		Left common carotid artery
19.	Brachial artery		Renal artery
20.	Ascending aorta		Middle cerebral artery

EXERCISE 3 - TRUE OR FALSE

The regular and rhythmic beating of the heart is ensured by the presence of a pacemaker that generates electrical impulses and a conducting system to transmit them. Which of the following statements about this system are correct? Mark as T or F accordingly.

21. The AV (atrioventricular) node serves as the primary pacemaker of the heart.

22. The cardiac pacemaker generates impulses faster than other areas of the heart.

23. The internodal conduction pathways connect the SA (sinoatrial) and AV nodes.

24. The SA node is located in the left atrium.

25. The bundle of His arises from the AV node.

26. In pacemaker action potential, rapid depolarization (Phase 0) is caused by K^+ influx.

27. In pacemaker action potential, repolarization (Phase 3) is caused by Ca^{++} efflux.

28. In pacemaker action potential, at the end of repolarization, slow influx of Na^+ gives rise to the "funny" current.

29. Ventricular action potential has a distinct plateau phase (Phase 2).

30. In ventricular action potential, depolarization (Phase 0) is dependent on the opening of voltage gated Na^+ channels.

EXERCISE 4 - FILL IN THE BLANKS

The electrical activity of the heart can be recorded and interpreted through electrocardiography (ECG). Knowing the basics of ECG is crucial in understanding cardiac rhythm abnormalities (arrhythmias).

31. On the ECG graph paper, each small square on the vertical axis equals

    _____ mV.

32. On the ECG graph paper, each small square on the horizontal axis

    equals _____ s.

33. The P wave represents _____.

34. A normal PR interval should be between _____ s.

35. The T wave represents _____.

36. The positive terminal of the limb lead I is placed on the

    _____.

37. The three limb leads, I, II and III, form the _____

    triangle.

38. Einthoven's law states that: Lead I + _____ = Lead II.

39. Leads V1-V6 are known as the _____ leads.

40. Lead V6 is placed on the _____ line in the 5th

    intercostal space.

EXERCISE 5 - MCQs

41. Which one of the following veins carries oxygenated blood?

    a. Femoral vein
    b. Inferior vena cava
    c. Pulmonary vein
    d. Hepatic vein

42. The muscular wall of the heart is also called its:

    a. Epicardium
    b. Myocardium
    c. Endocardium
    d. Sarcolemma

43. The endocardium is continuous with the:

    a. Epicardium
    b. Mediastinum
    c. Endothelium
    d. Cardiac apex

44. The pericardial cavity is a space between the visceral pericardium (the epicardium) and the:

    a. Pleura
    b. Mediastinum
    c. Parietal pericardium
    d. Endocardium

45. Venous blood returning from the myocardium reaches the right atrium through the:

    a. Superior vena cava
    b. Inferior vena cava
    c. Coronary sinus
    d. Renal vein

46. The left atrioventricular valve of the heart is also called the:

    a. Bicuspid valve
    b. Mitral valve
    c. Tricuspid valve
    d. Both a and b

47. Which heart chamber has the thickest walls?

    a. Right atrium
    b. Right ventricle
    c. Left atrium
    d. Left ventricle

48. The rapid spread of action potential between cardiac muscle cells is facilitated by the presence of:

    a. Connective tissue
    b. Basement membrane
    c. Gap junctions
    d. Z lines

49. The normal rhythm of the heart is also referred to as:

    a. Eupnea
    b. Peristalsis
    c. Sinus rhythm
    d. Bradycardia

50. Which one of the following valves is open during systole?

    a. Tricuspid valve
    b. Bicuspid valve
    c. Mitral valve
    d. Pulmonary valve

51. Cardiac output is a product of heart rate and:

   a.   Ejection fraction
   b.   Stroke volume
   c.   Venous return
   d.   Atrial systole

52. Atrial systole occurs near the end of:

   a.   Ventricular systole
   b.   Ventricular diastole
   c.   Inspiration
   d.   Expiration

53. Which one of the following valves is a type of semilunar valve?

   a.   Tricuspid valve
   b.   Bicuspid valve
   c.   Mitral valve
   d.   Pulmonary valve

54. Closure of which one of the following valves contributes to the 'dub' part of the heart's lub-dub sound?

   a.   Tricuspid valve
   b.   Bicuspid valve
   c.   Mitral valve
   d.   Pulmonary valve

55. The walls of arteries and veins are made up of several layers. Which one of the following layers of blood vessels contains smooth muscle?

   a.   Tunica externa
   b.   Tunica media
   c.   Tunica intima
   d.   Endothelium

UNIT IV

Respiratory System

EXERCISE 1 - LABEL THE PICTURE

The respiratory system is divided into the upper and lower respiratory tracts. Can you name their major structures?

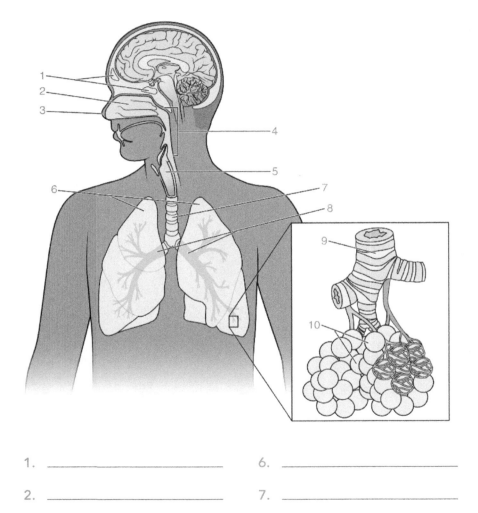

1. _____   6. _____

2. _____   7. _____

3. _____   8. _____

4. _____   9. _____

5. _____   10. _____

EXERCISE 2 – MATCH THE COLUMNS

Several respiratory volumes and capacities have been defined for the lungs.
Can you match their names with their definitions?

	Name	Correct match	Definition
11.	Lung volume		Maximum air volume forcibly inspired after tidal inspiration
12.	Lung capacity		Air volume left in lungs after forced expiration
13.	Tidal volume		Total volume of air in the lungs, both exchangeable and nonexchangeable
14.	Inspiratory reserve volume		Calculated value, cannot be directly measured with a spirometer
15.	Expiratory reserve volume		Total air volume left in lungs after tidal expiration
16.	Residual volume		Air volume exchanged during each breath
17.	Inspiratory capacity		Total volume of air in the lungs that is exchangeable
18.	Vital capacity		Maximum air volume forcibly expired after tidal expiration
19.	Functional residual capacity		Can be measured directly with a spirometer
20.	Total lung capacity		Total volume of air that can be inspired

EXERCISE 3 - TRUE OR FALSE

The nose and paranasal sinuses are the main structures that make up the upper respiratory tract. Which of the following statements are correct about them? Mark with T or F accordingly.

21. The sense of smell is also known as olfaction.

22. The nasal cavity is divided into two halves by the nasal septum.

23. Excessive tears drain into the nose through the nasolacrimal duct.

24. Nasal hair in the nostrils prevent the entry of large particles into the respiratory system.

25. The paranasal sinuses are lined with olfactory epithelium.

26. The frontal sinus is the largest of the paranasal sinuses.

27. The paranasal sinuses are normally filled with mucus.

28. All of the paranasal sinuses open into the nasal cavity.

29. Inflammation of the sinuses is called sinusitis.

30. The sphenoid sinus is located in the ethmoid bone.

EXERCISE 4 - FILL IN THE BLANKS

The lung was designed and built for gas exchange—acquiring oxygen and releasing carbon dioxide for the body. The following questions test your knowledge of the principals of gas exchange in the lung.

31. Gas exchange takes place in the _____ of the lung.

32. Alveolar clusters are organized into functional units called _____.

33. The alveolar epithelium is primarily made up _____ cells.

34. Surfactant is stored and secreted by _____ alveolar epithelial cells.

35. The general typical value for the ventilation-perfusion (V/Q) ratio of the lung is _____.

36. The V/Q ratio is _____ toward the apex of the lung compared to its base.

37. One liter of blood can carry about _____ mL of oxygen.

38. Gas exchange between the alveoli and blood occurs by _____.

39. The oxygen-hemoglobin dissociation curve depicts the relation between hemoglobin oxygen saturation and the _____ of oxygen in blood.

40. Conditions that shift the oxygen-hemoglobin dissociation curve to the left _____ the oxygen affinity of hemoglobin.

31

EXERCISE 5 - MCQs

41. Regular, restful breathing is controlled by:

    a. Midbrain
    b. Pons
    c. Medulla oblongata
    d. Thalamus

42. Which one of the following is a broad skeletal muscle that covers the thoracic cavity from below and assists in respiration?

    a. Platysma
    b. Trapezius
    c. Diaphragm
    d. Intercostal muscle

43. When lung volume increases, the pressure inside decreases. This leads to:

    a. Respiration
    b. Inspiration
    c. Expiration
    d. Coughing

44. Which one of the following is a passive process?

    a. Respiration
    b. Inspiration
    c. Expiration
    d. Coughing

45. Which one of the following sequence pairs is NOT correct?

    a. Primary bronchi → Secondary bronchi
    b. Secondary bronchi → Bronchioles
    c. Bronchioles → Alveolar ducts
    d. Alveolar ducts → Alveoli

46. Which one of the following are cells in the lungs that produce mucus?

    a. Langerhans cells
    b. Type I alveolar cells
    c. Goblet cells
    d. Endothelial cells

47. The right lung has three lobes. How many lobes does the left lung have?

    a. 1
    b. 2
    c. 3
    d. 4

48. The space between the two lungs is called:

    a. Pericardial space
    b. Intercostal space
    c. Parietal pleura
    d. Mediastinum

49. At its lower end, the laryngopharynx continues into the:

    a. Larynx
    b. Trachea
    c. Oral cavity
    d. Esophagus

50. The Eustachian tube connects the middle ear with the:

    a. Nasal cavity
    b. Nasopharynx
    c. Oropharynx
    d. Laryngopharynx

51. Which one of the following is called the voice box?

    a. Maxillary sinus
    b. Epiglottis
    c. Larynx
    d. Pharynx

52. Which one of the following laryngeal cartilages forms the Adam's apple?

    a. Thyroid
    b. Cricoid
    c. Arytenoid
    d. Epiglottis

53. Men generally have a lower pitch than women. This is because their vocal cords are:

    a. Stronger
    b. Longer
    c. Shorter
    d. Faster

54. Compared to the partial pressure of CO_2 in air, the partial pressure of CO_2 in deoxygenated blood is:

    a. Zero
    b. Lower
    c. Higher
    d. The same

55. Bronchial arteries most commonly arise from:

    a. Vertebral artery
    b. Pulmonary artery
    c. Subclavian artery
    d. Descending thoracic aorta

UNIT V

Gastrointestinal System

EXERCISE 1 – LABEL THE PICTURE

The liver and biliary tract are key components of the digestive system. Are you familiar with the anatomy in this region?

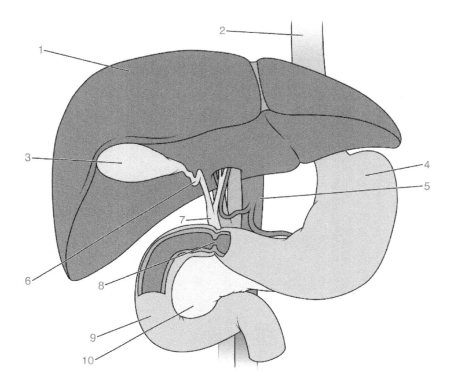

1. _____   6. _____

2. _____   7. _____

3. _____   8. _____

4. _____   9. _____

5. _____   10. _____

EXERCISE 2 – MATCH THE COLUMNS

Gastrointestinal hormones have a multitude of important effects. Can you match the following hormones with their action?

	Hormone	Correct match	Action
11.	Gastrin		Stimulates appetite
12.	Gastrin-releasing peptide (GRP)		Insulin secretion
13.	Gastric inhibitory peptide (GIP)		Increases gut motility
14.	Somatostatin		Gastric acid and pepsinogen secretion
15.	Cholecystokinin		Gastric smooth muscle relaxation
16.	Secretin		Inhibits pancreatic and gastric secretions
17.	Ghrelin		Hunger inhibition
18.	Motilin		Gastrin release
19.	Vasoactive intestinal peptide (VIP)		Pancreatic secretion of bicarbonate
20.	Leptin		Gall bladder contraction and pancreatic secretion

EXERCISE 3 - TRUE OR FALSE

Digestion involves the breakdown of large molecules in food into smaller ones. This essentially requires enzymes. Which of the following statements are true about digestive enzymes?

21. Salivary amylase initiates lipid digestion in the mouth.

22. Another name for salivary amylase is ptyalin.

23. Lysozyme in saliva can kill bacteria.

24. Gastric lipase is an acidic lipase compared with pancreatic lipase which is an alkaline lipase.

25. Pancreatic lipase converts triglycerides to monoglycerides and free fatty acids.

26. Bile assists in protein digestion through a process called emulsification.

27. Pancreatic lipase functions optimally in the presence of its coenzyme, colipase.

28. Chymotrypsin is the inactive form of trypsin.

29. Trypsin hydrolyzes proteins.

30. Without lactase, milk cannot be completely digested.

EXERCISE 4 – FILL IN THE BLANKS

The nervous system of the gastrointestinal tract, the enteric nervous system, is so evolved and extensive that it is termed as the second brain. Test your knowledge about it with the following questions.

31. The enteric nervous system includes two plexuses: the submucosal plexus and the _____ plexus.

32. In general, sympathetic stimulation _____ gastrointestinal motor activity.

33. Parasympathetic innervation to the stomach is supplied by the _____ nerve.

34. The enterogastric reflex _____ gastric motility and the secretion of gastrin.

35. Gastric distention gives rise to the _____ reflex.

36. Duodenal distension and increased acidity give rise to the _____ reflex.

37. The gastrocolic reflex causes the urge to _____ following a meal.

38. The gastroileal reflex leads to the opening of the _____ valve.

39. _____ contractions help mix up chyme with intestinal secretions.

40. Peristalsis normally occurs in a _____ direction.

EXERCISE 5 - MCQs

41. The digestive tract is also known as the:

   a.   Elementary canal
   b.   Alimentary canal
   c.   Food pipe
   d.   All of the above

42. Which one of the following terms means swallowing?

   a.   Egestion
   b.   Emesis
   c.   Deglutition
   d.   Dysphagia

43. The first temporary set of teeth, or baby teeth, is also known as:

   a.   Deciduous teeth
   b.   Permanent teeth
   c.   Molars
   d.   Alveolar arch

44. How many canine teeth do we have in each jaw?

   a.   2
   b.   4
   c.   6
   d.   8

45. The part of the tooth that projects above the gum is called:

   a.   Root
   b.   Neck
   c.   Crown
   d.   Gingivae

46. Which one of the following is the largest salivary gland?

   a.   Lingual
   b.   Sublingual
   c.   Submandibular
   d.   Parotid

47. The mucosa of the stomach is thrown into folds called:

   a.   Villi
   b.   Rugae
   c.   Pylorus
   d.   Papillae

48. Which one of following cell types in the stomach secretes HCl?

   a.   Mucus cells
   b.   Chief cells
   c.   Parietal cells
   d.   All of the above

49. The pancreatic duct joins the:

   a.   Duodenum
   b.   Jejunum
   c.   Ileum
   d.   Common bile duct

50. Each villus contains a central lymph vessel called:

   a.   Chyle
   b.   Microvillus
   c.   Lacteal
   d.   Thoracic duct

51. The small intestine is held in place by a fold of peritoneum called:

    a. Greater omentum
    b. Falciform ligament
    c. Mesentery
    d. Mesocolon

52. Which one of the following folds of peritoneum is known to wall off infections?

    a. Greater omentum
    b. Falciform ligament
    c. Mesentery
    d. Mesocolon

53. Which one of the following folds of peritoneum divides the liver into a large right lobe and a small left lobe?

    a. Greater omentum
    b. Falciform ligament
    c. Mesentery
    d. Mesocolon

54. Cells in the hepatic sinusoids that phagocytize bacteria are called:

    a. Langerhans cells
    b. Hepatocytes
    c. Kupffer cells
    d. Parietal cells

55. The endocrine part of the pancreas is made up by cluster of cells called:

    a. Tail of pancreas
    b. Peyer's patches
    c. Langerhans cells
    d. Islets of Langerhans

Nervous System

EXERCISE 1 - LABEL THE PICTURE

The brain is the seat of intelligence and consciousness. Can you correctly identify its parts pointed to in the image below?

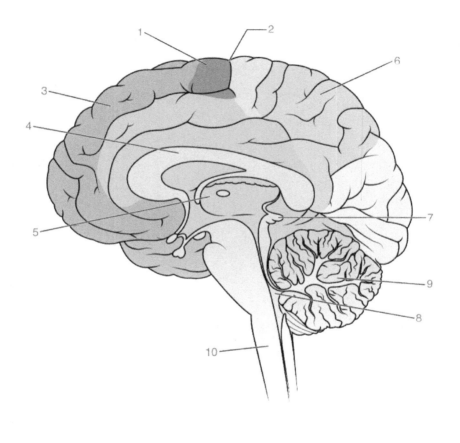

1. _____   6. _____

2. _____   7. _____

3. _____   8. _____

4. _____   9. _____

5. _____   10. _____

EXERCISE 2 - MATCH THE COLUMNS

Different areas of the brain are linked to specific functions. Can you match each of the following structure of the brain to its proposed role?

	Structure	Correct match	Function
11.	Cerebrum		Hunger, thirst and temperature control
12.	Corpus callosum		Coordination of fine muscle movement and balance
13.	Thalamus		Regulates endocrine glands
14.	Hypothalamus		Thinking, consciousness, voluntary movement
15.	Cerebellum		Regulates breathing and circulation
16.	Hippocampus		Relay center
17.	Pituitary gland		Sleep and arousal
18.	Reticular formation		Simple reflexes
19.	Medulla oblongata		Information bridge between the two cerebral hemispheres
20.	Spinal cord		Part of limbic system, role in learning and memory

EXERCISE 3 - TRUE OR FALSE

The central nervous system is made up of the brain and spinal cord. Which of the following statements about the spinal cord are correct? Mark with T or F accordingly.

21. The spinal cord emerges from the foramen magnum as a continuation of the medulla oblongata.

22. It occupies the full length of the vertebral column in adults.

23. The central canal of the spinal cord contains synovial fluid.

24. The spinal cord is enlarged in the cervical and lumbar regions.

25. There are a total of 21 pairs of spinal nerves.

26. There are seven pairs of cervical nerves.

27. The ventral root of a spinal nerve is efferent, that is, it carries motor information from the brain to the muscles.

28. A lumbar puncture is made into the epidural space around the spinal cord.

29. On cross section, the grey matter of the spinal cord is shaped like a butterfly.

30. The corticospinal tract enables voluntary movement of the body and limbs.

EXERCISE 4 - FILL IN THE BLANKS

The autonomic nervous system is an essential component of the peripheral nervous system. Test your knowledge of it with the following questions.

31. The autonomic nervous system (ANS) innervates the internal organs, smooth muscle and _____.

32. It is called the autonomic nervous system because its actions are _____.

33. The central control of the autonomic nervous system in the brain occurs at the _____.

34. The _____ division of the autonomic nervous system is referred to as the "fight or flight" system.

35. The _____ division of the autonomic nervous system is referred to as the "rest and digest" system.

36. The _____ division of the autonomic nervous system has a "craniosacral outflow".

37. In general, _____ ganglia are located closer to their target organs.

38. All splanchnic nerves carry sympathetic fibers except the _____ splanchnic nerves, which carry parasympathetic fibers.

39. Pupillary dilatation is a _____ effect.

40. Bronchodilation is a _____ effect.

EXERCISE 5 - MCQs

41. Our body's response to a stimulus is carried out by effector organs. Our main effector organs are muscles and:

    a. Brain
    b. Skin
    c. Glands
    d. Gut

42. Which one of the following four types of neurons are mostly motor (or efferent) in nature?

    a. Multipolar
    b. Unipolar
    c. Bipolar
    d. Anaxonic

43. Which one of the following four types of neurons are mostly sensory (or afferent) in nature?

    a. Multipolar
    b. Unipolar
    c. Bipolar
    d. Anaxonic

44. How many pairs of cranial nerves are there?

    a. 6
    b. 12
    c. 18
    d. 24

45. In nerves, the connective tissue covering of individual fibers is called:

    a. Endoneurium
    b. Fasciculus
    c. Perineurium
    d. Epineurium

46. Which one of the following types of glial cells take part in the formation of the blood-brain barrier?

    a. Astrocytes
    b. Ependyma
    c. Microglia
    d. Oligodendrocytes

47. Which one of the following types of glial cells is involved in phagocytosis?

    a. Astrocytes
    b. Ependyma
    c. Microglia
    d. Oligodendrocytes

48. Which one of the following types of glial cells form myelin sheaths?

    a. Astrocytes
    b. Ependyma
    c. Microglia
    d. Oligodendrocytes

49. In their resting state, compared to the outside, the inside of neurons is more:

    a. Positive
    b. Negative
    c. Neutral
    d. Hypertonic

50. A depolarization of a neuron will only be propagated if it overcomes:

    a. Resting potential
    b. Threshold potential
    c. Repolarization
    d. Na+ influx

51. Excessive K+ efflux during repolarization of a neuron leads to its:

    a. Depolarization
    b. Threshold potential
    c. Hyperpolarization
    d. Resting potential

52. Myelin sheaths help to speed up impulse conduction in nerve fibers through a process called:

    a. Reinforcement
    b. Excitation
    c. Saltatory conduction
    d. Endplate potential

53. Neurotransmitter release from the presynaptic nerve terminal requires influx of which ions?

    a. Na^+
    b. K^+
    c. Ca^{2+}
    d. Cl-

54. Cerebrospinal fluid (CSF) is produced by:

    a. Circle of Willis
    b. Arachnoid mater
    c. Choroid plexus
    d. Fourth ventricle

55. Which cerebral lobe contains the primary visual cortex?

    a. Frontal
    b. Parietal
    c. Temporal
    d. Occipital

Endocrine System

EXERCISE 1 - LABEL THE PICTURE

The following illustration shows the major structures of the endocrine system. Can you label them?

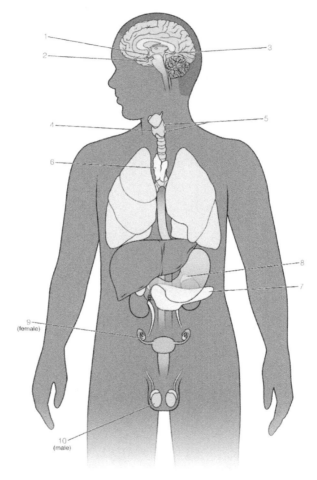

1. _____	6. _____
2. _____	7. _____
3. _____	8. _____
4. _____	9. _____
5. _____	10. _____

EXERCISE 2 - MATCH THE COLUMNS

Hormones perform many important functions in the body. Can you match the following hormones with their actions?

	Hormone	Correct match	Action
11.	Calcitonin		Decreases blood glucose
12.	Thyroxine		Male secondary sex characteristics
13.	Parathormone		Stress response
14.	Insulin		Blood pressure regulation
15.	Cortisol		Inhibits calcium release from bones
16.	Glucagon		Female secondary sex characteristics
17.	Testosterone		Regulates metabolism
18.	Aldosterone		Increases blood glucose
19.	Estrogen		Sleep cycle
20.	Melatonin		Stimulates calcium release from bones

EXERCISE 3 - TRUE OR FALSE

The pituitary gland is the "master" gland of the endocrine system. Which of the following statements about it are true? Mark with T or F accordingly.

21. The anterior lobe of the pituitary gland is also known as the neurohypophysis.

22. The anterior pituitary originates from a projection of the oral ectoderm called the Rathke's pouch.

23. The hypophyseal fossa lies in the middle of the occipital bone.

24. Regulatory hormones from the hypothalamus reach the anterior pituitary through the hypothalamo-hypophyseal portal system.

25. Somatotropes in the anterior pituitary secrete growth hormone.

26. Prolactin is released from the posterior pituitary.

27. Oxytocin is released by the posterior pituitary but it is formed in the hypothalamus.

28. Antidiuretic hormone (ADH) is also known as somatostatin.

29. Thyroid-stimulating hormone (TSH) from the hypothalamus stimulates the release of thyrotropin-releasing hormone (TRH) from the anterior pituitary.

30. An increase in the secretion of melanocyte-stimulating hormone (MSH) will cause darker skin color in humans.

EXERCISE 4 - FILL IN THE BLANKS

While most of the pancreas is organized to function as an exocrine gland, its islets of Langerhans secrete the all-important insulin and glucagon. These hormones have a fundamental role in the regulation of blood glucose in the body. Test your knowledge of blood glucose regulation with the following exercise.

31. The delta cells of the islets of Langerhans produce _____.

32. The alpha cells of the islets of Langerhans produce _____.

33. In type 1 diabetes, the _____ cells of the islets of Langerhans are selectively destroyed by autoimmune processes.

34. A normal fasting blood glucose level should be _____ mg/dL or lower.

35. A normal A1C should be below _____.

36. The _____ does not need insulin to utilize glucose.

37. _____ is a term which means low blood glucose level.

38. Excess glucose is stored in the liver in the form of _____.

39. Glucagon _____ blood glucose levels.

40. _____, which is co-secreted with insulin, slows gastric emptying and promotes satiety.

EXERCISE 5 - MCQs

41. Which one of the following is NOT a steroid hormone?

   a.   Estrogen
   b.   Testosterone
   c.   Insulin
   d.   Cortisol

42. Which one of the following hormones is a modified amino acid?

   a.   Epinephrine
   b.   Oxytocin
   c.   Luteinizing hormone
   d.   Growth hormone

43. Which one of the following hormones can cross the cell membrane and does not need a cell surface receptor?

   a.   Luteinizing hormone
   b.   Growth hormone
   c.   Insulin
   d.   Cortisol

44. Chromaffin cells of the adrenal medulla secrete:

   a.   Aldosterone
   b.   Epinephrine
   c.   Cortisol
   d.   Androgens

45. Excess of which one of the following hormones can cause virilism in females?

   a.   Aldosterone
   b.   Epinephrine
   c.   Cortisol
   d.   Androgens

46. Which one of the following is considered a part of the sympathetic nervous system?

   a. Adenohypophysis
   b. Thymus
   c. Adrenal medulla
   d. Spleen

47. Which one of the following is the active form of the thyroid hormone?

   a. T3
   b. T4
   c. Thyroxine
   d. Thyrotropin

48. The parafollicular cells (C cells) of the thyroid gland secrete:

   a. Parathormone
   b. Chymotrypsin
   c. Thyroxine
   d. Calcitonin

49. The thymus plays a role in the development of:

   a. Thyroid hormones
   b. Tetany
   c. T lymphocytes
   d. Thoracic duct

50. Corticotropin-releasing hormone (CRH) is produced by the:

   a. Adrenal cortex
   b. Adrenal medulla
   c. Anterior pituitary
   d. Hypothalamus

51. Levels of all of the following hormones increase during stress EXCEPT:

    a. Cortisol
    b. Epinephrine
    c. Gonadotropins
    d. Vasopressin

52. The body's stress response is initiated and controlled by the:

    a. Hypothalamus
    b. Anterior pituitary
    c. Adrenal cortex
    d. Adrenal medulla

53. Growth hormone has all of the following metabolic effects EXCEPT:

    a. Protein anabolism
    b. Insulin resistance
    c. Fat deposition
    d. Sodium retention

54. Thyroid hormone has all of the following metabolic effects EXCEPT:

    a. Increases basal metabolic rate (BMR)
    b. Increases thermogenesis
    c. Increases fat deposition
    d. Increases gluconeogenesis

55. All of the following hormones are anabolic EXCEPT:

    a. Growth hormone
    b. Cortisol
    c. Testosterone
    d. Insulin

Blood and Immune System

EXERCISE 1 - LABEL THE PICTURE

The following image shows the different stages of hematopoiesis. Can you name the numbered blood cells?

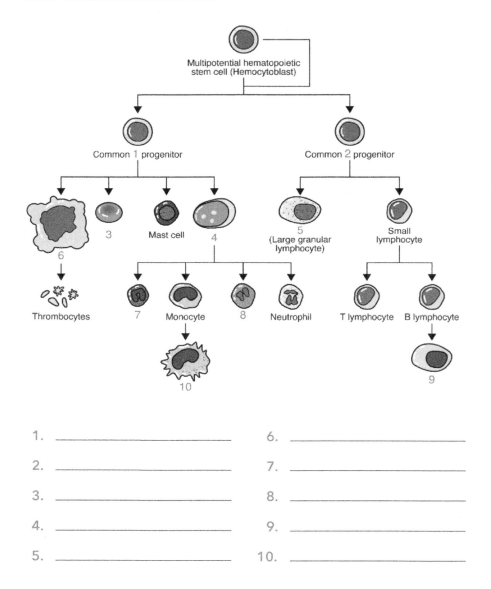

1. _____   6. _____

2. _____   7. _____

3. _____   8. _____

4. _____   9. _____

5. _____   10. _____

EXERCISE 2 - MATCH THE COLUMNS

A complete blood count is one of the most common lab tests performed. Can you match the parameters with their correct values in the following table? To simplify, the values are given for adult men.

	Parameter	Correct match	Value
11.	Hematocrit (%)		4.09-11.00
12.	Hemoglobin (g/L)		0.00-0.09
13.	Red blood cells (1012/L)		1.3-3.6
14.	Leucocytes (109/L)		134-167
15.	Neutrophils (109/L)		0.23-0.73
16.	Eosinophils (109/L)		4.38-5.65
17.	Basophils (109/L)		172-398
18.	Lymphocytes (109/L)		39.2-48.6
19.	Monocytes (109/L)		0.05-0.55
20.	Platelets (109/L)		1.78-6.95

EXERCISE 3 – TRUE OR FALSE

Red blood cells are our body's oxygen transporting vehicles. Are the following statements correct about them? Mark with T or F accordingly.

21. Red blood cells are also called erythrocytes.

22. Erythrocytes are red because they contain carotene.

23. A mature red blood cell is shaped like a biconvex disk.

24. Mature red blood cells do not contain a nucleus.

25. The lifespan of red blood cells is up to 120 days.

26. People living at high altitudes, where there is low oxygen tension, have fewer red blood cells than the rest of the population.

27. Each hemoglobin molecule contains six heme groups

28. Red blood cells have rigid and inflexible membranes to maintain a consistent shape.

29. The spleen is called the graveyard of red blood cells.

30. Erythrocytes contain abundant mitochondria.

EXERCISE 4 – FILL IN THE BLANKS

Antibodies are at the forefront of the fight against pathogens. In scientific terms, they confer on us humoral immunity. Can you answer the following questions about this type of immunity?

31. Another term for an antibody is _____.

32. In terms of molecular structure, antibodies are _____-shaped.

33. The five types of antibody are: IgA, _____, IgE, IgG and IgM.

34. Antibodies are produced and released by _____, which in turn are activated B cells.

35. Each antibody has the ability to detect and bind to a specific _____.

36. _____ cells facilitate the conversion of B cells into plasma cells.

37. The antibody type most abundantly associated with mucosal membranes and their secretions, including tears and saliva, is _____.

38. The antibody type most frequently associated with allergic diseases is _____.

39. The antibody type that is the main antibody found in blood is _____.

40. The antibody type that is the largest in size is _____

EXERCISE 5 - MCQs

41. The most common form of white blood cell in the body is:

     a.   B cells
     b.   Neutrophils
     c.   Eosinophils
     d.   Thrombocytes

42. Which one of the following cells is most abundant in pus?

     a.   B cells
     b.   Neutrophils
     c.   Eosinophils
     d.   Thrombocytes

43. Which one of the following is a process responsible for the migration of leucocytes to the site of infection?

     a.   Phagocytosis
     b.   Amebiasis
     c.   Chemotaxis
     d.   Metastasis

44. Which one of the following cells is frequently associated with the development of allergic responses?

     a.   Natural killer cells
     b.   Neutrophils
     c.   Eosinophils
     d.   Thrombocytes

45. Which one of the following cells produces major basic protein (MBP) which is responsible for many of the cell's effects?

     a.   Natural killer cells
     b.   Neutrophils
     c.   Eosinophils
     d.   Thrombocytes

46. The 'respiratory burst' is an important mechanism by which phagocytic cells destroy bacteria. Which enzyme is necessary to initiate this process?

    a. Na^+-K^+ ATPase
    b. DNA polymerase
    c. Pyruvate kinase
    d. NADPH oxidase

47. The body's process that attempts to stop bleeding is called:

    a. Homeostasis
    b. Hemostasis
    c. Hematopoiesis
    d. Hemorrhage

48. Von Willebrand factor (VWF) is necessary to produce which one of the following?

    a. Vasoconstriction
    b. Platelet plug
    c. Blood clot
    d. Phagosome

49. Vitamin K is necessary for the normal formation of which of the following clotting factors?

    a. Prothrombin (factor II)
    b. Factors VII, IX and X
    c. Proteins C, S and Z
    d. All of the above

50. Which one of the following acts directly on fibrinogen to convert it into fibrin?

    a. Prothrombin
    b. Thrombin
    c. Factor X
    d. Calcium ions

51. Which one of the following is clotting factor I?

    a. Prothrombin
    b. Fibrinogen
    c. Calcium ions
    d. Tissue factor

52. Which one of the following is clotting factor IV?

    a. Prothrombin
    b. Fibrinogen
    c. Calcium ions
    d. Tissue factor

53. Which clotting factor is deficient in hemophilia A?

    a. VII
    b. VIII
    c. IX
    d. X

54. Hemophilia is transmitted through which chromosome?

    a. 14
    b. 21
    c. X
    d. Y

55. Low levels of factor XI causes:

    a. Hemophilia A
    b. Hemophilia B
    c. Hemophilia C
    d. Von Willebrand disease

Urinary System

EXERCISE 1 - LABEL THE PICTURE

The nephron is the basic structural and functional unit of urine production. Can you name its different parts?

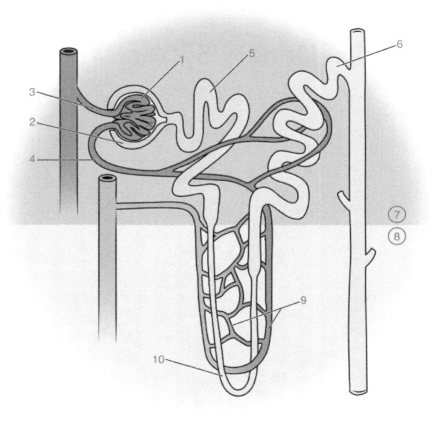

1. _____   6. _____

2. _____   7. _____

3. _____   8. _____

4. _____   9. _____

5. _____   10. _____

EXERCISE 2 – MATCH THE COLUMNS

The kidney has a close relationship with hormones. Some it produces, some act on it. Can you match the following hormones with their action?

	Hormone	Correct match	Action
11.	Renin		Increases calcium reabsorption at distal tubule.
12.	Erythropoietin		Increases sodium reabsorption at distal tubule.
13.	Calcitriol		Increases sodium reabsorption at proximal tubule.
14.	Aldosterone		Increases sodium excretion at collecting duct.
15.	Angiotensin II		Formed in the kidney. Assists platelet production.
16.	Atrial natriuretic peptide		Formed in the kidney. Creates angiotensin I.
17.	Antidiuretic hormone		Formed in the kidney. Active form of Vitamin D.
18.	Thrombopoietin		Formed in kidney. Assists red blood cell synthesis.
19.	Parathyroid hormone		Decreases the reabsorption of calcium.
20.	Calcitonin		Increases water reabsorption at collecting duct.

EXERCISE 3 - TRUE OR FALSE

While urine formation occurs in the kidneys, the urinary tract also includes the ureters, bladder and urethra which help transport the urine out of the body. Which of the following statements about these three structures are correct?

21. Transitional epithelium, also known as urothelium, lines the inside of the ureters and bladder.

22. The transitional epithelium appears cuboidal when stretched.

23. The ureters begin at the renal cortex.

24. In males, the bladder is located on top of the prostate gland.

25. The trigone of the bladder is made up of the urethral and two ureteric orifices.

26. The detrusor muscle of the bladders consists of striated muscle fibers.

27. Urination is also known as micturition, voiding and uresis.

28. The micturition center in the brain is located in the medulla oblongata.

29. In infants, micturition is an involuntary reflex.

30. The external urethral sphincter enables voluntary control over urination, while the internal urethral sphincter is involuntary.

EXERCISE 4 - FILL IN THE BLANKS

Urine formation is an intricate process occurring at the level of each individual nephron. Here are some questions about it.

31. The chief steps of urine formation are: glomerular filtration, tubular reabsorption and _____.

32. Glomerular filtrate contains little if any plasma _____.

33. The volume of filtrate formed over a certain time is expressed as the _____.

34. Tubular reabsorption begins in the _____.

35. Amino acids and glucose are almost completely reabsorbed in the _____.

36. Most of the sodium in the filtrate is reabsorbed in the _____.

37. The loop of Henle and _____ form the countercurrent multiplier system.

38. The countercurrent multiplier system acts to increase the concentrations of Na^+ and _____ deep in the medulla.

39. In the collecting duct, the _____ cells play an important role in acid-base homeostasis.

40. In the collecting duct, _____ increases aquaporin channels to promote water reabsorption.

EXERCISE 5 – MCQs

41. Which one of the following functions can be attributed to the urinary system?

    a.   Osmolality regulation
    b.   Acid-base balance
    c.   Blood pressure maintenance
    d.   All of the above

42. The kidneys maintain acid-base balance by secreting hydrogen ions into the urine and reabsorbing:

    a.   Sodium ions
    b.   Water
    c.   Bicarbonate ions
    d.   Urea

43. The kidney acts as a target organ to maintain plasma osmolality. Any substantial increase in plasma osmolality is detected by the:

    a.   Adrenal gland
    b.   Adenohypophysis
    c.   Hypothalamus
    d.   Bladder

44. The renal vein drains into the:

    a.   Common iliac vein
    b.   Hepatic vein
    c.   Inferior vena cava
    d.   Coronary sinus

45. The tips of the renal pyramids are called:

    a.   Renal columns
    b.   Renal calyces
    c.   Renal hilum
    d.   Renal papillae

46. What percent of the cardiac output goes to the kidneys?

    a.   10-15%
    b.   15-20%
    c.   20-25%
    d.   25-30%

47. Juxtaglomerular cells (JG cells) of the kidney:

    a.   Reabsorb water
    b.   Reabsorb amino acids
    c.   Produce renin
    d.   Secrete creatinine

48. Which one of the following can activate the renin-angiotensin system (RAS)?

    a.   Drop in blood pressure
    b.   Loss of blood volume
    c.   Decrease in renal blood flow
    d.   All of the above

49. Angiotensinogen is produced by the:

    a.   Liver
    b.   Lung
    c.   Heart
    d.   Kidney

50. ACE (angiotensin converting enzyme) mainly occurs in the:

    a.   Liver
    b.   Lung
    c.   Heart
    d.   Kidney

51. In an empty bladder, its inner lining is thrown into folds called:

    a. Rugae
    b. Papillae
    c. Trigone
    d. Villi

52. The process of tubular secretion begins in the:

    a. Proximal convoluted tubule
    b. Loop of Henle
    c. Distal convoluted tubule
    d. Collecting duct

53. Which one of the following is commonly used to estimate glomerular filtration rate (GFR)?

    a. Glucose
    b. Chlorine
    c. Creatinine
    d. Glycine

54. Vasa recta arise from:

    a. Renal artery
    b. Loop of Henle
    c. Afferent arteriole
    d. Efferent arteriole

55. Which one of the following is the primary mechanism by which most clinical drugs are eliminated by the kidney?

    a. Tubular secretion
    b. Tubular reabsorption
    c. Countercurrent exchange
    d. Glomerular filtration

Reproductive System

EXERCISE 1 - LABEL THE PICTURE

The menstrual cycle involves cyclic changes at different levels. The following image is a schematic illustration of those cyclic changes. Can you label it?

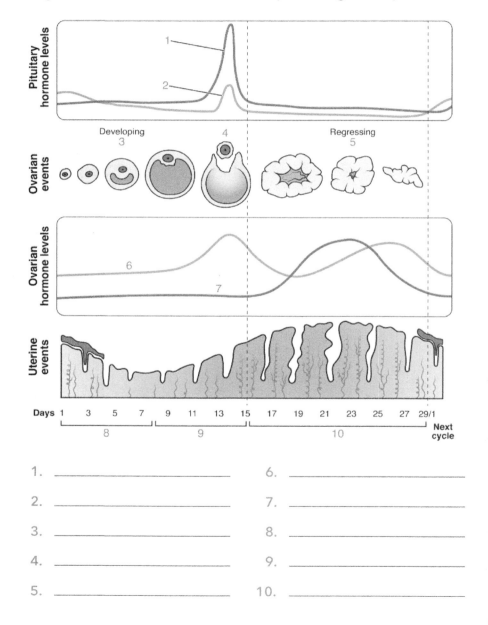

1. _____   6. _____

2. _____   7. _____

3. _____   8. _____

4. _____   9. _____

5. _____   10. _____

EXERCISE 2 - MATCH THE COLUMNS

Reproductive physiology runs on a collection of hormones. Can you match the following hormones with their actions?

	Hormone	Correct match	Action
11.	Gonadotropin-releasing hormone (GnRH)		Endometrial proliferation.
12.	Luteinizing hormone (LH)—female		Stimulates testosterone production.
13.	Follicle stimulating hormone (FSH)—female		Uterine contraction, milk letdown.
14.	Estrogen—female		Follicular maturation and ovulation.
15.	Progesterone—female		Inhibits FSH secretion in men.
16.	Oxytocin—female		Prepares endometrium for implantation.
17.	Luteinizing hormone (LH)—male		Stimulates secretion of LH and FSH.
18.	Follicle stimulating hormone (FSH)—male		Secondary sexual characteristics in men.
19.	Testosterone—male		Follicular development.
20.	Inibin—male		Supports spermatogenesis.

EXERCISE 3 – TRUE OR FALSE

Which of the following statements about the anatomy of the female reproductive system are correct? Mark with T or F accordingly.

21. The mesovarium is the part of the broad ligament of the uterus that suspends the ovaries.

22. The medulla of the ovary is rich in ovarian follicles.

23. The surface of the ovary is covered by stratified squamous epithelium.

24. The fimbriae are finger-like projections of the fallopian tube at its ovarian end.

25. The inner mucosa of the fallopian tubes is lined with ciliated columnar epithelium.

26. The narrow part of the fallopian tubes that connects to the uterus is called ampulla.

27. The top of the uterus is known as its fundus.

28. The normal uterus is anteverted as well as anteflexed.

29. The thick smooth muscle layer of the uterus is called its endometrium.

30. The ectocervix is the part of the cervix that projects into the vagina.

EXERCISE 4 - FILL IN THE BLANKS

Test your knowledge of the anatomy of the male reproductive system with the following questions.

31. During fetal development, the testes descend through the _____ to reach the scrotum.

32. The _____ cells in the testis produce testosterone.

33. The serous covering of the testis is called _____.

34. The tail of the epididymis continues as the _____.

35. The _____ is a layer of muscle within the wall of the scrotum that consists of smooth muscle fibers.

36. Stroking the upper, inner part of the thigh elevates the testis. This is known as the _____ reflex.

37. The testicular artery is a branch of the _____.

38. The ejaculatory duct is formed by the union of the vas deferens and _____.

39. The prostate gland lies in front of the _____.

40. The prostatic ducts open into the _____.

EXERCISE 5 - MCQs

41. The dartos muscle of the scrotum has a role in:

    a. Ejaculation
    b. Micturition
    c. Temperature regulation
    d. Hormone production

42. The fibrous tissue covering of the testis is called:

    a. Tunica albuginea
    b. Scrotum
    c. Epididymis
    d. Hydrocele

43. Spermatogonia produce sperms through:

    a. Mitosis
    b. Meiosis
    c. Budding
    d. Replication

44. The Sertoli cells of the seminiferous tubules are activated by:

    a. Luteinizing hormone (LH)
    b. Follicle stimulating hormone (FSH)
    c. Testosterone
    d. Inibin

45. Most of the fluid in semen is derived from the:

    a. Prostate
    b. Seminal vesicles
    c. Testes
    d. Epididymis

46. The fallopian tubes are also known as:

    a. Uterine tubes
    b. Oviducts
    c. Salpinges
    d. All of the above

47. Which section of the fallopian tubes is most commonly the site of fertilization?

    a. Infundibulum
    b. Ampulla
    c. Isthmus
    d. Intramural section

48. Which one of the following is the predominant form of estrogen in females?

    a. Estrone
    b. Estradiol
    c. Estriol
    d. Estetrol

49. Until the onset of puberty, primary oocytes in the ovary are suspended in:

    a. Prophase I
    b. Metaphase I
    c. Metaphase II
    d. Interphase

50. After ovulation but before fertilization, the oocyte is arrested in:

    a. Prophase I
    b. Metaphase I
    c. Metaphase II
    d. Interphase

51. If two follicles mature and ovulate, which one of the following would be the more likely result?

    a.   Fraternal twins

    b.   Identical twins

    c.   Monozygotic twins

    d.   Polar twins

52. Which hormone triggers ovulation?

    a.   Luteinizing hormone (LH)

    b.   Follicle stimulating hormone (FSH)

    c.   Estrogen

    d.   Progesterone

53. Which one of the following has a key role in preventing polyspermy?

    a.   Corpus luteum

    b.   Corona radiata

    c.   Zona pellucida

    d.   Cumulus oophorus

54. Which one of the following does not contain an oocyte?

    a.   Corpus luteum

    b.   Corona radiata

    c.   Zona pellucida

    d.   Cumulus oophorus

55. After ovulation, if not fertilized, the egg is viable for about how many hours?

    a.   12

    b.   24

    c.   36

    d.   48

Answers

UNIT I
Cell, Cell Membrane and Nucleic Acids

EXERCISE 1 – LABEL THE PICTURE

1. Space of Disse
2. Smooth/agranular endoplasmic reticulum
3. Rough/granular reticulum
4. Golgi complex
5. Bile canaliculus
6. Cell membrane
7. Lysosomes
8. Nucleus/nuclear membrane
9. Microbody
10. Mitochondrion

EXERCISE 2 – MATCH THE COLUMNS

11. Barrier and transport
12. Energy synthesis
13. Protein synthesis
14. Transport and packaging
15. Regulation and cell division

16. Digestion
17. Shape and movement
18. Detoxification
19. Ribosomal assembly
20. Lipid synthesis

EXERCISE 3 – TRUE OR FALSE

21. F

    R: The cell membrane and cell wall are different structures. While all cells have cell membranes, some cells, for example, those belonging to bacteria and plants, have a covering in addition to and lying outer to the cell membrane. It is called the cell wall. The structure and properties of the cell wall are different than the cell membrane.

22. T
23. F
   R: The phospholipid bilayer structure of the cell membrane creates a hydrophobic barrier. Small uncharged molecules, such as CO_2 and O_2, and lipid soluble molecules, such as ethanol, can cross it easily via passive diffusion.
24. T
25. T
26. T
27. T
28. F
   R: The cell membrane of nerve cells doesn't have a special name. Remember, another name for a nerve cell is a neuron. Its cell membrane can just be called a cell membrane, plasma membrane or neuronal membrane. Sarcolemma is the name given to the cell membrane of striated muscle fibers. Another term, neurilemma, is the outermost covering of axons of neurons in the peripheral nervous system. It is made up Schwann cells. It is a different structure than the cell membrane of the neuron itself.

29. F
   R: As explained above, in the rationale for question 23, small uncharged molecules, such as CO_2 and O_2, can pass freely through the cell membrane via passive diffusion. Therefore, oxygen does not need any special transport protein to move it across the cell membrane.
30. T

EXERCISE 4 - FILL IN THE BLANKS

31. nucleic
32. phosphate
33. deoxyribose
34. cytosine
35. uracil
36. nucleus/cell nucleus
37. viruses
38. double
39. Transcription
40. transfer RNA (tRNA)

EXERCISE 5 - MCQs

41. d
42. c
43. b
44. b
45. c
46. b
47. c
48. c
49. a
50. d
51. b
52. d
53. c
54. c
55. d

UNIT II
Skin and Musculoskeletal System

EXERCISE 1 - LABEL THE PICTURE

1. Iliac crest
2. Sacroiliac joint
3. Pelvic inlet
4. Ilium
5. Pubic bone
6. Ischial spine
7. Femur
8. Ischium/ischial tuberosity
9. Pubic symphysis
10. Hip joint

EXERCISE 2 - MATCH THE COLUMNS

11. Musculocutaneous
12. Axillary
13. Thoracodorsal
14. Long thoracic
15. Accessory
16. Radial
17. Median
18. Radial, deep branch
19. Ulnar
20. Ulnar, deep branch

EXERCISE 3 - TRUE OR FALSE

21. T
22. F
    R: The two layers of the skin are epidermis and dermis. The hypodermis is technically not a layer of the skin although it is usually included as its third layer.

23. F
    R: Pacinian corpuscles sense deep pressure. Changes in temperature are detected by free nerve endings in the skin.

24. T
25. F
    R: Stratum corneum is thick and contains keratin. Stratum lucidum is a translucent layer containing the protein eleidin.

26. T
27. T
28. F
    R: Nociception is the perception of **pain**.

29. F
    R: There are two types of sweat glands: eccrine and apocrine. The common type that occurs all over the body is eccrine. Apocrine occurs in armpits and the external genital area.

30. F
    R: Nails are hard because of **keratin**.

EXERCISE 4 - FILL IN THE BLANKS

31. arthrology
32. synarthroses
33. all/three
34. abduction
35. knee
36. teeth
37. hyaline
38. brachialis
39. tibia
40. hinge

EXERCISE 5 - MCQs

41. c	49. d
42. c	50. a
43. c	51. d
44. d	52. d
45. c	53. c
46. c	54. b
47. d	55. b
48. b	

UNIT III
Cardiovascular System

EXERCISE 1 - LABEL THE PICTURE

1. Aorta
2. Pulmonary artery
3. Pulmonary veins
4. Pulmonary valve
5. Right atrium
6. Tricuspid valve
7. Right ventricle
8. Inferior vena cava
9. Interventricular septum
10. Apex

EXERCISE 2 - MATCH THE COLUMNS

11. Anterior tibial artery
12. Maxillary artery
13. Middle cerebral artery
14. Renal artery
15. Lateral thoracic artery
16. Left common carotid artery
17. Superior gluteal artery
18. Vertebral artery
19. Radial artery
20. Right coronary artery

EXERCISE 3 - TRUE OR FALSE

21. F

    R: The SA (sinoatrial) node serves as the primary pacemaker of the heart as it has the fastest rate. The SA node has an intrinsic rate of 60–100 bpm, while the rate of the AV node is 40–60 bpm.

22. T
23. T
24. F

    R: The SA node is located in the **right** atrium.

25. T
26. F

    R: In pacemaker action potential, rapid depolarization (Phase 0) is caused by **Ca++ influx**.
27. F

    R: In pacemaker action potential, repolarization (Phase 3) is caused by **K+ efflux**.
28. T
29. T
30. T

EXERCISE 4 – FILL IN THE BLANKS

31. 0.1
32. 0.04
33. atrial depolarization

34. 0.12-0.20
35. ventricular repolarization
36. left arm
37. Einthoven's
38. Lead III
39. chest/precordial
40. mid-axillary

EXERCISE 5 – MCQs

41. c
42. b
43. c
44. c
45. c
46. d
47. d
48. c

49. c
50. d
51. b
52. b
53. d
54. d
55. b

UNIT IV
Respiratory System

EXERCISE 1 – LABEL THE PICTURE

1. Paranasal sinuses
2. Nasal cavity/turbinate/concha
3. Nose
4. Pharynx
5. Larynx
6. Lungs
7. Trachea
8. Bronchi
9. Bronchiole
10. Alveoli

EXERCISE 2 – MATCH THE COLUMNS

11. Can be measured directly with a spirometer
12. Calculated value, cannot be directly measured with a spirometer
13. Air volume exchanged during each breath
14. Maximum air volume forcibly inspired after tidal inspiration

15. Maximum air volume forcibly expired after tidal expiration
16. Air volume left in lungs after forced expiration
17. Total volume of air that can be inspired
18. Total volume of air in the lungs that is exchangeable
19. Total air volume left in lungs after tidal expiration
20. Total volume of air in the lungs, both exchangeable and nonexchangeable

EXERCISE 3 - TRUE OR FALSE

21. T
22. T
23. T
24. T
25. F
    R: The paranasal sinuses are lined with the respiratory epithelium. The olfactory epithelium is limited to the roof of the nasal cavity and is linked to olfaction.
26. F
    R: The **maxillary sinus** is the largest of the paranasal sinuses.
27. F
    R: The paranasal sinuses are normally filled with **air**.
28. T
29. T
30. F
    R: The paranasal sinuses are named after the bones in which they are found. Therefore, the sphenoid sinus must be located in the sphenoid bone.

EXERCISE 4 - FILL IN THE BLANKS

31. alveoli
32. acini
33. simple squamous/type I alveolar
34. type II
35. 0.8
36. higher
37. 200
38. simple, passive diffusion
39. partial pressure
40. increase

EXERCISE 5 - MCQs

41. b	49. d
42. c	50. b
43. b	51. c
44. c	52. a
45. b	53. b
46. c	54. c
47. b	55. d
48. d	

UNIT V
Gastrointestinal System

EXERCISE 1 - LABEL THE PICTURE
1. Liver
2. Esophagus
3. Gall bladder
4. Stomach
5. Aorta/abdominal aorta
6. Cystic duct
7. Common bile duct
8. Pylorus/pyloric sphincter
9. Duodenum
10. Pancreas

EXERCISE 2 - MATCH THE COLUMNS
11. Gastric acid and pepsinogen secretion
12. Gastrin release
13. Insulin secretion
14. Inhibits pancreatic and gastric secretions
15. Gall bladder contraction and pancreatic secretion
16. Pancreatic secretion of bicarbonate
17. Stimulates appetite
18. Increases gut motility
19. Gastric smooth muscle relaxation
20. Hunger inhibition

EXERCISE 3 - TRUE OR FALSE
21. F
    R: Salivary amylase initiates **carbohydrate/starch** digestion in the mouth.

22. T
23. T
24. T
25. T
26. F
    R: Bile assists in **lipid/fat** digestion through a process called emulsification.
27. T
28. F
    R: Chymotrypsin and trypsin are separate enzymes though they have a similar structure. Both are active forms. Their inactive forms are chymotrypsinogen and trypsinogen, respectively.
29. T
30. T

EXERCISE 4 - FILL IN THE BLANKS
31. myenteric
32. inhibits
33. vagus
34. inhibits
35. gastrocolic
36. enterogastric
37. defecate
38. ileocecal
39. Segmentation
40. caudal/aboral

EXERCISE 5 - MCQs

41. b	46. d	51. c
42. c	47. b	52. a
43. a	48. c	53. b
44. a	49. d	54. c
45. c	50. c	55. d

UNIT VI
Nervous System

EXERCISE 1 - LABEL THE PICTURE

1. Precentral
2. Central
3. Frontal
4. Corpus callosum
5. Thalamus
6. Parietal
7. Pineal
8. Fourth
9. Cerebellum
10. Medulla oblongata

EXERCISE 2 - MATCH THE COLUMNS

11. Thinking, consciousness, voluntary movement
12. Information bridge between the two cerebral hemispheres
13. Relay center
14. Hunger, thirst and temperature control
15. Coordination of fine muscle movement and balance
16. Part of limbic system, role in learning and memory
17. Regulates endocrine glands
18. Sleep and arousal
19. Regulates breathing and circulation
20. Simple reflexes

EXERCISE 3 - TRUE OR FALSE

21. T
22. F

    R: The spinal cord is shorter than the vertebral column and ends at the level of the second lumbar vertebra.
23. F

    R: The central canal of the spinal cord contains **cerebrospinal** fluid.
24. T
25. F

    R: There are a total of **31 pairs** of spinal nerves.

26. F

R: There are eight pairs of cervical nerves although there are seven cervical vertebrae.

27. T

28. F

R: A lumbar puncture is made into the **subarachnoid space** around the spinal cord.

29. T

30. T

EXERCISE 4 - FILL IN THE BLANKS

31. glands
32. involuntary/unconscious
33. hypothalamus

34. sympathetic
35. parasympathetic
36. parasympathetic
37. parasympathetic
38. pelvic
39. sympathetic
40. sympathetic

EXERCISE 5 - MCQs

41. c	49. b
42. a	50. b
43. b	51. c
44. b	52. c
45. a	53. c
46. a	54. c
47. c	55. d
48. d	

UNIT VII
Endocrine System

EXERCISE 1 - LABEL THE PICTURE

1. Hypothalamus
2. Pituitary gland
3. Pineal gland
4. Thyroid gland
5. Parathyroid glands
6. Thymus
7. Pancreas
8. Adrenal gland
9. Ovary
10. Testis

EXERCISE 2 - MATCH THE COLUMNS

11. Inhibits calcium release from bones
12. Regulates metabolism
13. Stimulates calcium release from bones
14. Decreases blood glucose
15. Stress response
16. Increases blood glucose
17. Male secondary sex characteristics

18. Blood pressure regulation
19. Female secondary sex characteristics
20. Sleep cycle

EXERCISE 3 - TRUE OR FALSE

21. F

    R: The anterior lobe of the pituitary gland is also known as the adenohypophysis. The neurohypophysis is the other name of the posterior pituitary.

22. T
23. F

    R: The hypophyseal fossa lies in the middle of the **sphenoid** bone.

24. T
25. T
26. F

    R: Prolactin is released from the **anterior** pituitary.

27. T
28. F

    R: Antidiuretic hormone (ADH) is also known as **vasopressin**.

29. F

    R: It is the other way around. Thyrotropin-releasing hormone (TRH) from the hypothalamus stimulates the release of thyroid-stimulating hormone (TSH) from the anterior pituitary.

30. T

EXERCISE 4 - FILL IN THE BLANKS

31. somatostatin
32. glucagon
33. beta
34. 99
35. 5.7%
36. brain
37. Hypoglycemia
38. glycogen
39. elevates/raises
40. Amylin

EXERCISE 5 - MCQs

41. c
42. a
43. d
44. b
45. d
46. c
47. a
48. d
49. c
50. d
51. c
52. a
53. c
54. c
55. b

UNIT VIII
Blood and Immune System

EXERCISE 1 – LABEL THE PICTURE

1. myeloid
2. lymphoid
3. Erythrocyte/red blood cell
4. Myeloblast
5. Natural killer cell
6. Megakaryocyte
7. Basophil
8. Eosinophil
9. Plasma cell
10. Macrophage

EXERCISE 2 – MATCH THE COLUMNS

11. 39.2-48.6
12. 134-167
13. 4.38-5.65
14. 4.09-11.00
15. 1.78-6.95
16. 0.05-0.55
17. 0.00-0.09
18. 1.3-3.6
19. 0.23-0.73
20. 172-398

EXERCISE 3 – TRUE OR FALSE

21. T
22. F

    R: Erythrocytes are red because they contain **hemoglobin**.

23. F

    R: A mature red blood cell is shaped like a **biconcave** disk.

24. T
25. T
26. F

    R: In fact, they have higher red blood cell counts to compensate for the low oxygen tension. It is a part of their body's adaptation response to living at high altitudes.

27. F

    R: Each hemoglobin molecule contains **four** heme groups.

28. F

    R: It's the opposite. The membrane of red blood cells, owing to its structure and the presence of certain proteins, makes them quite deformable, flexible and durable. This is necessary as red blood cells have to squeeze through capillaries that have a diameter smaller than them.

29. T
30. F

    R: Erythrocytes **do not** contain mitochondria.

EXERCISE 4 - FILL IN THE BLANKS

31. immunoglobulin (Ig)
32. Y
33. IgD
34. plasma cells
35. antigen
36. Helper T
37. IgA
38. IgE
39. IgG
40. IgM

EXERCISE 5 - MCQs

41. b
42. b
43. c
44. c
45. c
46. d
47. b
48. b
49. d
50. b
51. b
52. c
53. b
54. c
55. c

UNIT IX
Urinary System

EXERCISE 1 - LABEL THE PICTURE

1. Glomerulus
2. Bowman's capsule
3. Afferent arteriole
4. Efferent arteriole
5. Proximal convoluted tubule
6. Distal convoluted tubule
7. Cortex
8. Medulla
9. Vasa recta
10. Loop of Henle

EXERCISE 2 - MATCH THE COLUMNS

11. Formed in the kidney. Creates angiotensin I.
12. Formed in kidney. Assists red blood cell synthesis.
13. Formed in the kidney. Active form of Vitamin D.
14. Increases sodium reabsorption at distal tubule.
15. Increases sodium reabsorption at proximal tubule.
16. Increases sodium excretion at collecting duct.
17. Increases water reabsorption at collecting duct.
18. Formed in the kidney. Assists platelet production.
19. Increases calcium reabsorption at distal tubule.
20. Decreases the reabsorption of calcium.

EXERCISE 3 - TRUE OR FALSE

21. T
22. F

    R: The transitional epithelium is a type of stratified epithelium that changes shape in response to stretch. It appears squamous when stretched and cuboidal when relaxed.
23. F

    R: The ureters begin at the renal **pelvis**.
24. T
25. T
26. F

    R: The detrusor muscle of the bladders consists of **smooth** muscle fibers.
27. T
28.
29. F

    R: The micturition center in the brain is located in the **pons**.
30. T
31. T

EXERCISE 4 - FILL IN THE BLANKS

32. tubular secretion
33. proteins
34. glomerular filtration rate (GFR)
35. proximal convoluted tubule
36. proximal convoluted tubule
37. proximal convoluted tubule
38. vasa recta
39. urea
40. intercalated
41. antidiuretic hormone (ADH)

EXERCISE 5 - MCQs

42.	d	50.	a
43.	c	51.	b
44.	c	52.	a
45.	c	53.	a
46.	d	54.	c
47.	c	55.	d
48.	c	56.	a
49.	d		

UNIT X
Reproductive System

EXERCISE 1 - LABEL THE PICTURE

1. Luteinizing hormone (LH)
2. Follicle stimulating hormone (FSH)
3. follicle
4. Ovulation
5. corpus luteum
6. Estrogen
7. Progesterone
8. Menstruation
9. Follicular phase
10. Luteal phase

EXERCISE 2 - MATCH THE COLUMNS

11. Stimulates secretion of LH and FSH.
12. Follicular maturation and ovulation.
13. Follicular development.
14. Endometrial proliferation.
15. Prepares endometrium for implantation.
16. Uterine contraction, milk letdown.
17. Stimulates testosterone production.
18. Supports spermatogenesis.
19. Secondary sexual characteristics in men.
20. Inhibits FSH secretion in men.

EXERCISE 3 - TRUE OR FALSE

21. T
22. F
    R: The ovary has an outer layer called the ovarian cortex and an inner ovarian medulla. The cortex contains all the ovarian follicles. The medulla does not contain follicles.
23. F
    R: The surface of the ovary is covered by simple cuboidal epithelium. It is called mesothelium, and sometimes germinal epithelium.
24. T
25. T
26. F
    R: The narrow part of the fallopian tubes that connects to the uterus is called isthmus.
27. T
28. T
29. F
    R: The thick smooth muscle layer of the uterus is called its myometrium. Endometrium is the inner lining of the uterus.
30. T

EXERCISE 4 - FILL IN THE BLANKS

31. inguinal canal
32. Leydig
33. tunica vaginalis
34. vas deferens
35. dartos
36. cremasteric
37. abdominal aorta
38. seminal vesicle duct
39. rectum
40. prostatic urethra

EXERCISE 5 - MCQs

41. c
42. a
43. b
44. b
45. b
46. d
47. b
48. b
49. a
50. c
51. a
52. a
53. c
54. a
55. b

JOIN OUR COMMUNITY

Medical Creations® is an educational company focused on providing study tools for Healthcare students.

You can find all of our products at this link: **www.medicalcreations.net**

If you have any questions or concerns please contact us:
hello@medicalcreations.net

We want to be as close as possible to our customers, that's why we are active on all the main Social Media platforms.

You can find us here:

Facebook **www.facebook.com/medicalcreations**
Instagram **www.instagram.com/medicalcreationsofficial**
Pinterest **www.pinterest.com/medicalcreations**
Website: **www.medicalcreations.net**

CHECK OUT OUR OTHER BOOKS

EKG/ECG Interpretation:
Everything you Need to Know
about the 12 - Lead ECG/
EKG Interpretation and How to
Diagnose and Treat Arrhythmias:
Workbook

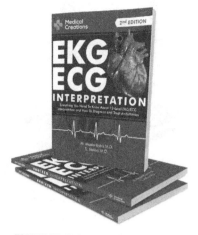

EKG/ECG Interpretation:
Everything you Need to Know
about the 12 - Lead ECG/EKG
Interpretation and How to
Diagnose and Treat Arrhythmias
(2nd Edition)

Scan the QR Code

Suture like a Surgeon:
A Doctor's Guide to Surgical Knots
and Suturing Techniques used in the
Departments of Surgery, Emergency
Medicine, and Family Medicine

**Advanced Cardiovascular
Life Support:**
Provider Manual - A
Comprehensive Guide Covering
the Latest Guidelines

**Advanced Cardiovascular
Life Support:**
Provider Manual - A
Comprehensive Guide Covering the
Latest Guidelines: Workbook

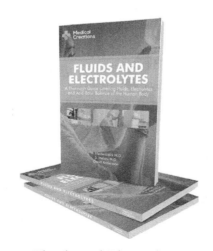

Fluids and Electrolytes:
A Torough Guide covering Fluids,
Electrolytes and Acid-Base Balance
of the Human Body

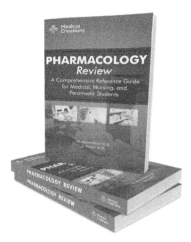

Pharmacology Review:
A Comprehensive Reference
Guide for Medical, Nursing, and
Paramedic Students

Pharmacology Review:
A Comprehensive Reference
Guide for Medical, Nursing, and
Paramedic Students: Workbook

DSM-5-TR:
A Broad Selection of Exercises
to Measure Your Psychiatry
Knowledge: Workbook

Medical Surgical Nursing:
Test your Knowledge with
Comprehensive Exercises in
Medical-Surgical Nursing:
Workbook

Lab Values:
Everything You Need to Know
about Laboratory Medicine and
its Importance in the Diagnosis
of Diseases

Basic Life Support:
Provider Manual - A
Comprehensive Guide Covering
the Latest Guidelines

Medical Creations Suture Practice Kit with Suturing Video Series
by Board-Certified Surgeon and Ebook Training Guide

SUTURE LIKE A SURGEON PRACTICE KIT

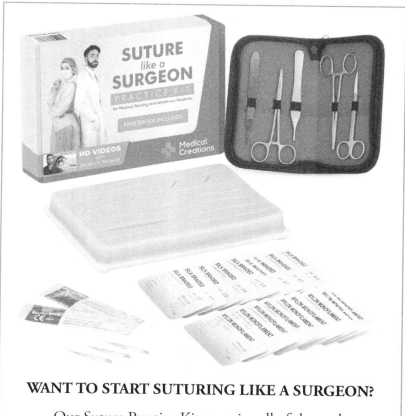

WANT TO START SUTURING LIKE A SURGEON?

Our Suture Practice Kit contains all of the tools
you need to start practicing.

Scan the QR Code

Made in the USA
Las Vegas, NV
21 September 2024

95601639R00066